D1452338

For Gene, Lauren, and Jakob -
thanks for being part of our hive.

Printed by Lightning Source Ltd.

Paperback ISBN: 978-1-7352363-4-6
Hardcover ISBN: 978-1-7352363-5-3

Scenic Route
Publishing
PO Box 2852
Kalamazoo, MI 49003

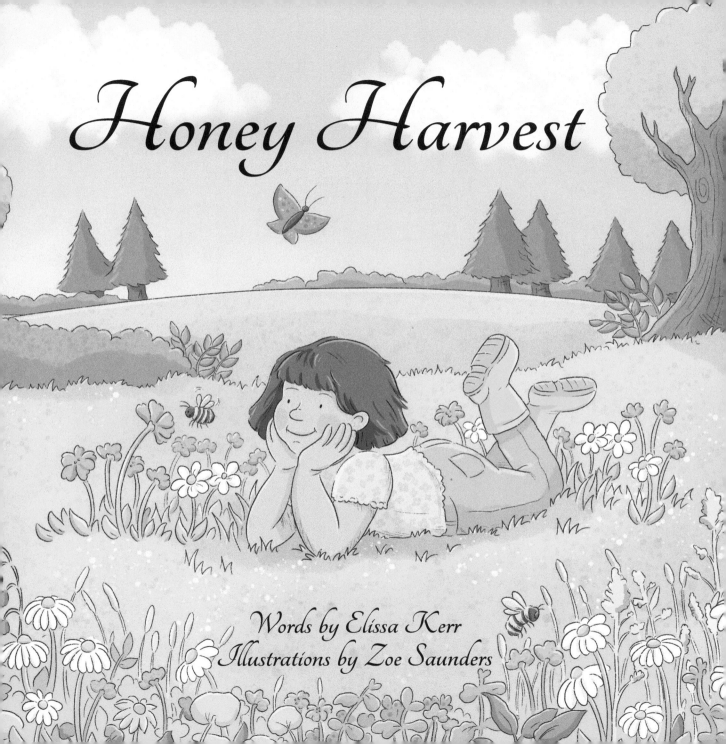

Honey Harvest

Words by Elissa Kerr
Illustrations by Zoe Saunders

One of my favorite things to eat
is a sweet and golden, sticky treat...

honey!

Drizzled on fruit or spread on toast,
I'm not sure how I like it most.

Stirred in yogurt or mixed in a smoothie,
there's countless options. No need to be choosy.

My dad gets honey from our hive,
but I have never seen inside.

Do all the bees wear tiny goggles?
All lined up, filling bear-shaped bottles.

A bustling factory production, buzzing along without interruption.

Today I get to help Dad out.
Let's see what this business is all about.

"Let's get ready."
I put on my veil and beekeeper suit.
It protects me from stings. "Don't I look cute?"

Dad slides on his gloves. We trek through the glen.
We cross fields of clover, bright flowers, and then...

The colony flies all around,
filling the air with a buzzing sound!

Dad uses his smoker to calm the bees.
He shows me how. I give it a squeeze.

He lifts the lid as I step near.
This is it! The big moment is here.

Wait... that all looks a bit funny.
I'm confused. "Where's the honey?"

I don't understand. I'm at a loss.
It's a wood box with slats across.

There are no jars, no factory, no spout.
"I thought the honey would just pour out."

Dad smiles at me, then simply explains,
"The honey is stored in each of these frames."

He pulls them out. Inspects each one.
"Our work has only just begun."

The bees fill up each frame with comb,
a hexagon structure that they call home.

"We won't take them all," my dad declares.
"The bees need to keep their own fair share."

We take the frames all capped in wax.
I brush bees off our modest stack.

Once our cart is full of comb,
Dad announces, "It's time to head home."

"What! That's it?" I say, dragging my feet.
This comb doesn't look like what I usually eat.

Dad chuckles as we both step inside.
He takes off his suit and sets it aside.

"This is our extractor," he says with a grin.
"Our frames will go for a nice little spin."

A hot knife scrapes the wax away.
I keep safe; this isn't play.

He trims each side till the wax is gone.
"The next step is one you can work on."

I carry each frame, dripping and sticky,
to the extractor, moving ever so quickly.

"Watch out. Here I come!"
I slide frames into the hollow drum.

When the comb is spun about,
all of the honey gets flung out.

Crank the handle! Give it a turn!
My face grows sweaty, and both arms burn.

I spin the handle a few strokes more,
and soon the honey is ready to pour.

Finally, the time has come
to open the valve and empty the drum.

Dad opens the gate so the honey will flow.
This is the treat I love and know.

We fill mason jars right up to the brim
before screwing on each metal rim.

I line them up. So clean and so neat.
Our honey harvest is almost complete.

The day is over, and the work's nearly done.
It's time to share with everyone.

A jar for Grandma, my teacher, a neighbor.
This is a treat that's bursting with flavor.

Sharing is fun... but it's not the best part.
I love helping my dad with something
close to his heart...

honey.

Frequently Asked Questions

How do I stay safe from bee stings?

There is a special piece of clothing you can wear. It is called a bee suit. A bee suit has long sleeves, long pants, and usually includes a veil or hood. When you put it on, be sure to check for gaps near your hands, feet, and neck. These are spots where bees can sneak into your suit. Slide on a pair of gloves and you are ready to work with bees.

When should I harvest honey?

Generally, it is a good idea to harvest honey at the end of summer. You can tell that the honey is ready when it is capped with beeswax. The frames should have at least 80% capped honeycomb to be harvested.

How much honey can I collect?

A strong hive will hold about 70-90 pounds of honey. This can change depending on the weather and the health of the bees. But remember you will not be harvesting all of it! If you take too much honey it can cause the colony to starve.

How do I store honey?

You can store honey for years as long as you keep it sealed at room temperature. While your honey will be stable for some time, many beekeepers recommend eating it within a year. This is not because the honey will go bad but because eating honey right away allows you to enjoy the best flavor possible. Yum!

About the Author

Elissa Kerr lives in Kalamazoo, Michigan, with her husband and her two sons. When she is not writing stories, you will probably find her spending time outdoors or taking nature walks. She does not have her own apiary yet. Honey Harvest is her third children's book.

Learn more about the author at www.scenicroutepublishing.com.

About the Illustrator

Zoe Saunders lives in Cheshire, Great Britain, with her husband, son, and daughter. She adores her work illustrating children's picture books and especially loves drawing nature and animals.

Learn more about the illustrator at www.whimsicolourart.com

9 781735 236353